Map Skills
for Key Stage 1

Pam Robson

The author, Pam Robson, is an experienced primary teacher with a particular interest in geography.

The consultant, Stephen Watts, is a teacher trainer at Sunderland University and a Fellow of the Royal Geographical Society.

Teachers' Notes

What is good classroom practice?

Ofsted inspection findings since 1992 highlight the need to integrate geographical skills into suitable real contexts. They also recommend that the teaching of geographical skills and investigations of places and themes should feed upon each other as part of one integrated scheme of work.

Relevant documents to consult are:

Ofsted   a Review of Inspection Findings – 1993/4

QCA   Expectations in Geography at Key Stages 1 and 2 – 1997

QCA   Geography and the Use of Language – 1997

In the light of the above recommendations, teachers should select worksheets that have relevance to real contexts, to which their pupils can relate. They should be used in conjunction with class investigations about particular places and themes rather than as isolated learning tools.

Literacy

Many of the activities included will be appropriate for use during the daily literacy hour and the hour of reading.

These include vocabulary work (using appropriate geographical vocabulary), alphabetical order (sequencing alphabetically using first and second letters of words), and using structural guiders (atlas index) to access information. Children are encouraged to use a variety of information sources to carry out their own research. There are also comprehension and writing activities requiring the interpretation of questions and instructions.

Familiar stories, like *Red Riding Hood* and *Goldilocks and the Three Bears*, feature as map activities. Children will need to be acquainted with these stories and should be encouraged to read and draw story maps.

An investigative approach

The focus of enquiry is indicated at the top of each sheet. Key questions then open up specific topics and themes to be investigated. On some sheets relevant discussion points are raised. Symbols highlight each area of activity:

Key:

 key question    investigation   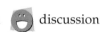 discussion

How to use this book

The worksheets have been structured in accordance with national curriculum requirements for Geography at KS1. Teachers will find that worksheets in the KS1 title will also be appropriate for children working at the early stages of KS2. Similarly worksheets in the KS2 book may also be appropriate for some children working at the later stages of KS1.

Teachers are advised to work progressively through the structured investigations. Alternatively, specific worksheets relating to one particular focus of enquiry can be selected if used in sequence.

Topic Web KS1
(with reference to National Curriculum requirements)

Geography
POS KS1

1 Investigate physical and human features of immediate surroundings.
2 Answer geographical questions e.g. Where is it?
3 Be aware that the world extends beyond the immediate locality.

Geographical Skills:

a recognising housing types
b mapping the school playground
c following directions using terms such as up, down, on, under, behind, in front of, near, far, left, right, north, south, east, west
d making maps of both real and imaginary places using pictures and symbols
e use globes, maps and plans at a variety of scales
f use secondary sources to obtain geographical information

Mathematics
POS KS1

a understanding the properties of shape
b understanding and use of properties of position and movement, describing positions using common words

c purposeful measuring / understanding and using measures / use simple measuring instruments / read and interpret numbers and scales

English
POS KS1 (Reading, Writing, and Speaking and Listening)

a read and listen to fairy stories
b use structural guiders e.g. contents and index to find out information
c write down instructions / directions
d follow instructions / directions
e understand questions
f talk about observations and experiences

> **Note for Teachers:** A useful optional classroom resource to use in conjunction with specified worksheets is the Evans' Atlas **All Around the World, An Illustrated Atlas** ISBN 0237 51631 4 - price £5.99. This atlas contains the relevant background information and visual references to support teachers; in particular Worksheets 17, 18, 19, 22, 25, 28, 29, 30, 32, 33, 34, 35, 36 and 38.

Teachers' checklist

Names	has undertaken fieldwork activities in the locality of the school	can follow directions, including up, down, on, under, behind, in front of, near, far, left, right, north, south, east, west	has made maps and plans of real and imaginary places, using pictures and symbols	has used globes, maps and plans at a variety of scales to identify cities, oceans and rivers	has located and named on a map of the UK its constituent countries	has marked approximately where s/he lives	has used secondary sources to obtain geographical information

Pupil's checklist   name:

....

1   I have drawn a story map.

The name of the story is...

These are pictures of my favourite characters:

2   I have drawn a route map. It shows my journey from home to school.

My mind picture of my route looks like this.

3   I have drawn a plan of the playground.

The playground measures.................................paces long.

The playground measures ....paces wide.

Where is it?

Where is the ball?

<u>in</u> the toy box   <u>on</u> the toy box   <u>under</u> the toy box   <u>near</u> the toy box

<u>far</u> from the toy box   <u>in front of</u> the toy box   <u>behind</u> the toy box

 Where is the car?

1 The car is . . . .
the toy box.

2 The car is . . . .
the toy box.

3 The car is . . . .
from the toy box.

4 The car is . . . .
the toy box.

5 The car is . . . .
the toy box.

6 The car is . . . .
the toy box.

7 The car is . . . .
the toy box.

 Look around you. Say where things are.

How do I explain where something is?

  Where are all the different objects?

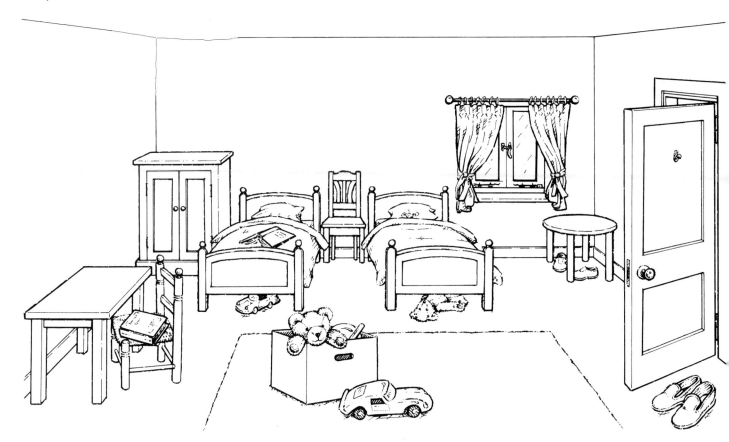

1 Colour the book on the chair yellow.

2 Colour the book on the bed red.

3 Colour the table near the window brown.

4 Colour the table near the cupboard black.

5 Colour the bear under the bed yellow.

6 Colour the bear in the toy box green.

7 Colour the slippers behind the door orange.

8 Colour the slippers under the table pink.

9 Colour the car in front of the toy box red.

10 Colour the car under the bed blue.

  Choose an object in the classroom and explain where it is to a friend. Ask your friend to guess the object.

Which way?

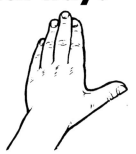

Hold up your left hand like this to make L for *Left*.
Are you left-handed?

Most people write with their *right* hand. Do you?

 Investigate which way to go . . .
Signposts tell us which way to turn. Left or right?

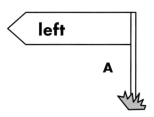

A

B

C

D

? ? ?

left

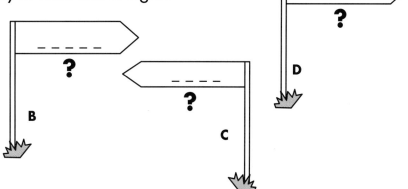

Find the way through the maze. Start at the arrow pointing *up*.
Then turn *left*.
Which way next?
Mark your way with arrows.

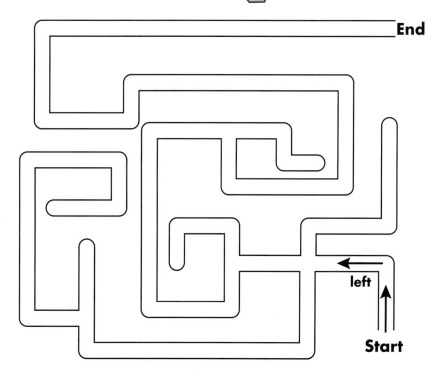

End

left

Start

 Use the words *left* and *right* to tell your friend the way from the classroom to the school library.

What do objects look like from above?

This is what you see . . .   This is what a bird sees . . .

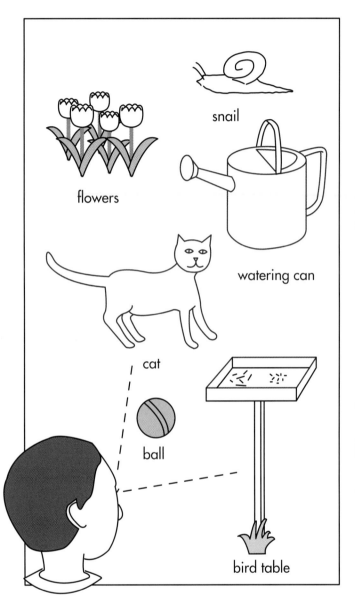

snail

flowers

watering can

cat

ball

bird table

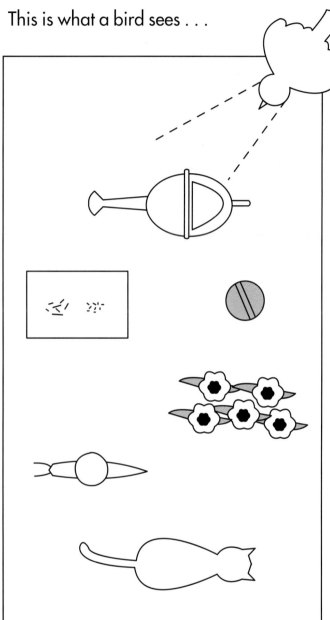

The bird in the air sees only the top of everything in the garden.
We call this a bird's eye view.

Draw lines joining each picture on the left with the correct bird's eye view
on the right.

 Choose two or three objects. What do you see when you look at them from the
side? Now look from above.

 Describe something you can see from above to a friend. Can she/he guess
what it is?

? **What is a plan?**

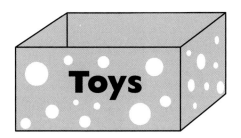

This is a **picture** of a toy box

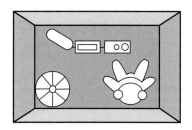

This is a **bird's eye view** of a toy box

To show the position of things we can draw a bird's eye view picture or *plan*.

  Look at the *picture* of the breakfast table.
Now look at the *plan* of the breakfast table.

Two objects are missing from the plan.
Draw in the missing objects.
Remember to draw them as if you were looking down from above.

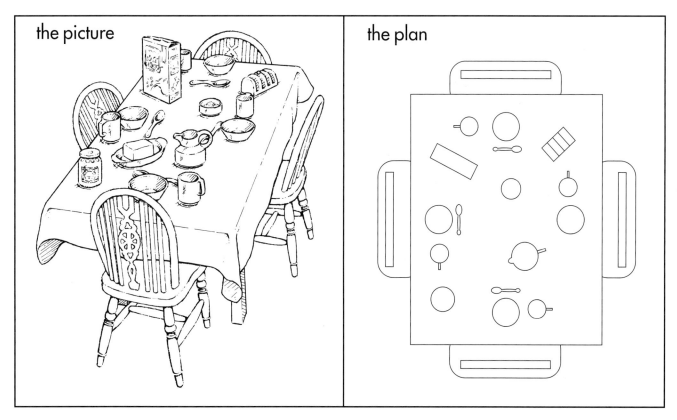

the picture

the plan

  Arrange some objects on your desk. Now draw what you see from above.
You have drawn a plan.

How do I draw a plan?

 Investigate this plan:

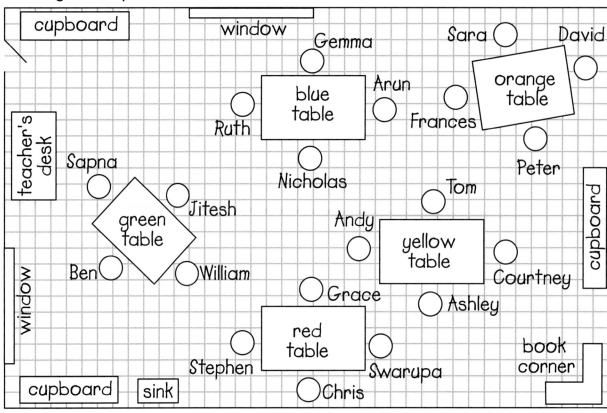

1 How many tables can you find? ....

2 How many cupboards can you find? ....

3 What is the colour of the table nearest to the teacher's desk? ....

4 What is the colour of the table nearest to the sink? ....

5 What is the colour of the table farthest from the sink? ....

6 Who sits on the right of Chris? ....

7 Who sits on the left of Chris? ....

8 Who sits behind Arun? ....

9 What is behind Courtney? ....

10 Who sits nearest to the teacher's desk? ....

 Look around your classroom. Now <u>sketch</u> a plan showing the position of the furniture. Use your sketch to draw a neat plan of your classroom on squared paper.

How do I describe the size of an object?

 Investigate the pictures to find the answers to the questions below.

1 Tree **A** is . . . . than tree **B**.
(bigger, smaller)

2 Tree **B** is . . . . than tree **A**.
(bigger, smaller)

big **small**

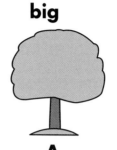

A B

biggest

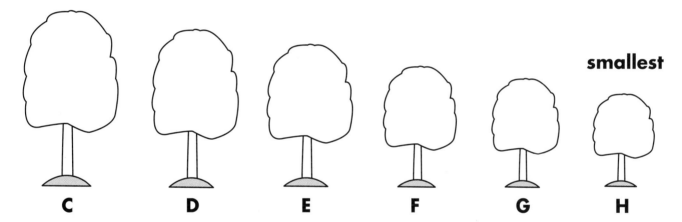

smallest

C   D   E   F   G   H

1 Which tree is the biggest? . . . .

2 Which tree is the smallest? . . . .

3 Colour green all the trees that are smaller than tree **E**.

4 Colour orange all the trees that are bigger than tree **F**.

These boxes are all different sizes.

1 Colour the biggest box yellow.

2 Colour the smallest box red.

3 Colour the middle-sized box blue.

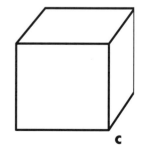

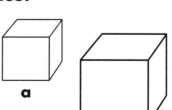

a b c

 There are many other words to describe size, such as *long, short, wide, narrow*. Look around you and describe the size of things that you see. If there are two similar things, like books, which one is the bigger?

How do I measure the size of objects?

Your eyes tell you that some things are big and some things are small. Look at the books on this bookshelf.

1 Colour the smallest book red.

2 Colour the biggest book green.

3 Colour the rest of the books yellow.

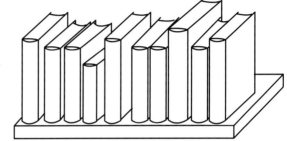

To <u>measure</u> *straight* things like books we can use toy bricks like this. Make sure the bricks are all the same size.

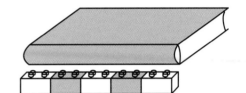

The book is . . . . toy bricks long.

We can use our hands to find the *size* of *big* things. Your hand is a good measuring tool.

Stretch your fingers wide and make a *hand span* like this.

From the top of your little finger to the top of your thumb is one hand span.

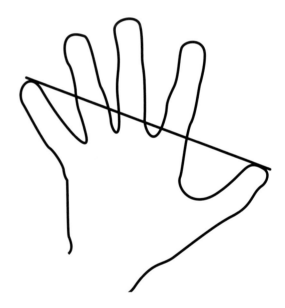

 Investigate your classroom.

1 Guess how many hand spans wide the classroom door is.   . . . . hand spans

2 Now *measure* how wide the door is in hand spans.   . . . . hand spans

3 Guess how many hand spans wide your table is.   . . . . hand spans

4 Now *measure* how wide your table is in hand spans.   . . . . hand spans

5 Is everyone's hand span the same size?   yes/no

  Draw around your hand span. Colour your drawing and cut it out. Ask your teacher to glue everyone's handspan drawing on to a large sheet of paper. Talk about who has the largest handspan. Who has the smallest?

Can I make an object look bigger or smaller without changing its shape?

Look at the big hand. This is the *real* size of a hand span. It has been drawn on centimetre squared paper. We call this a 1:1 scale.

 Put your hand on top of the hand span. Is your hand bigger or smaller than this one? Draw around your hand span on centimetre squared paper.

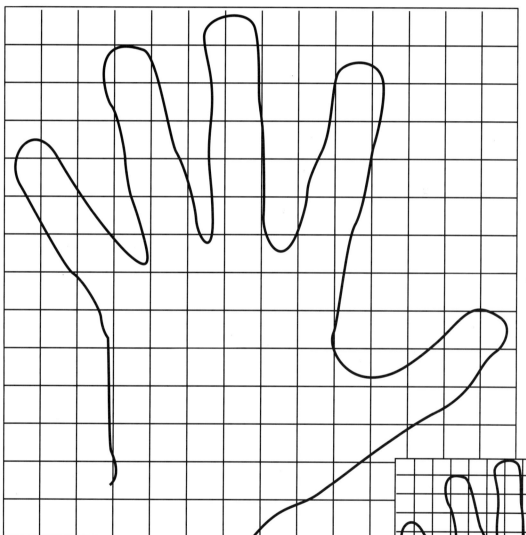

Below is a copy of the real hand span drawn on squared paper with *half* centimetre squares. It is *half* the real size. We call this 1:2 scale.

The real size is *twice* as big as the smaller hand span. The smaller hand span is *half* the size of the real hand span.

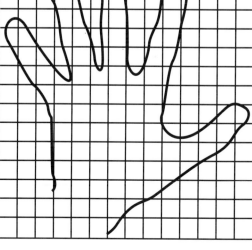

 Can you draw your hand span on half centimetre squared paper? Look carefully at the squares of your real hand span and copy the shape exactly on the smaller squares. Is the shape the same?

How do I use a centimetre ruler?

This is a long wriggly worm.

This is a short wriggly worm.

Your eyes tell you which worm is the longer of the two.
We cannot *measure* a wriggly worm *exactly* because it wriggles too much.

But we can measure *straight* lines *exactly*.
When we need to know *exactly* how long something is we use a *ruler* like this.

 Investigate a ruler.

| 0 | 1 | 2 | 3 | 4 | 5 | 6 | 7 | 8 | 9 | 10 | 11 | 12 | 13 | 14 | 15 |

Each space on the ruler is exactly 1 centimetre wide.

Measure with a ruler to find how long these toy bricks are.

a

. . . . centimetres

b

. . . . centimetres

c

. . . . centimetres

Measure these lines with a ruler.

A _____   . . . . centimetres

B _____   . . . . centimetres

C _____   . . . . centimetres

D _____   . . . . centimetres

Which is the longest line? . . . .

Which is the shortest line? . . . .

 Choose two or three books of different sizes. Use your ruler to measure exactly
how long each book is. Now measure how wide each book is. Which book is
longest? Which book is the widest?

? How do I draw a scale plan?

A plan is a bird's eye view picture.

A plan can show the shape and size of an object.

The book case has been measured in hand spans:

it is 8 hand spans long and 2 hand spans wide.

The book case is too big to draw its real size.

Instead we can use squared paper and draw a plan of the book case to *scale*.

The scale will be one square to 1 hand span.

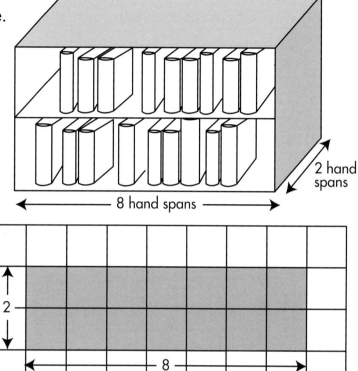

Scale: 1 square is really 1 hand span.

Now draw plans of these objects to scale.
They have been measured in hand spans.

1 The table is 4 hand spans wide and 7 hand spans long.

2 The book is 1 hand span wide and 2 hand spans long.

3 The cupboard is 3 hand spans wide and 10 hand spans long.

4 The toy box is 5 hand spans wide and 5 hand spans long.

Investigate your classroom. Choose a large object and measure it in hand spans. How wide is it? How long is it? Now draw it to scale.

Remember! 1 square is really 1 hand span.
You will need centimetre squared paper.
Count carefully the number of squares for each side of the shape.
Use a ruler.

Instead of measuring in hand spans, use a tape measure. Your measurements will be in centimetres. To draw the objects to scale you must decide how many centimetres each square on the paper will stand for. Try 1 square = 10 cm.

Can you estimate measurements?

Measure these lines with your ruler.

——   ———   ————   —————

1 centimetre   2 centimetres   3 centimetres   4 centimetres

Find a toy brick that looks 1 centimetre long.
Now check by measuring the brick with a ruler.

1 The brick *looks* 1 centimetre long.

The brick *measures* . . . . centimetres.

Find an object like a rubber that *looks* 2 centimetres long.
Now check by measuring the rubber with your ruler.

2 The rubber *looks* 2 centimetres long.

The rubber *measures* . . . . centimetres.

Investigate some bigger objects and guess how long they are. Then check your guesses by measuring with your ruler.

Look at each of these lines.
Estimate, or guess, how many centimetres long each line is. Then measure the lines with your ruler. Did you estimate correctly?

A ——————————   **B** ————

estimate: . . . . centimetres   estimate: . . . . centimetres

measurement: . . . . centimetres   measurement: . . . . centimetres

C ——

estimate: . . . . centimetres

measurement: . . . . centimetre

 On the back of this sheet, practise drawing lines with your ruler. Write how long each line is. Ask your friend to check your measurements with a ruler.

What are buildings used for?

Investigate buildings near your school.

All around us there are many different buildings.
A house is a building. It is also called a home.

semi-detached houses   a detached house   terraced houses

These buildings are also homes.

  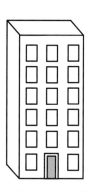

a bungalow   a cottage   a block of flats

Where do you live?

I live in a . . . .
(detached house, semi-detached house, terraced house, flat, bungalow, cottage)

What do people do in these buildings?

a   a supermarket

. . . .

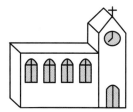
b   a church

. . . .

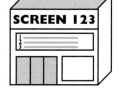
c   a cinema

. . . .

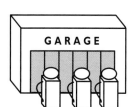
d   a garage

. . . .

Write beside each building what people do there.

a   go shopping   **b**   buy petrol   **c**   watch a film   **d**   say a prayer

How do I show buildings on a plan?

This is a bird's eye view picture, or plan, of a garage.

How many cars are there waiting in the garage? . . . .

How many petrol pumps can you see? . . . .

Investigate the pictures below.

Colour the block of flats yellow. Colour the church blue.
Colour the house red. Colour the supermarket orange.
Colour the cottage green.
Can you match up each picture of a building with the right plan?
Colour the plan to match the building.

A house

B supermarket

C block of flats

D church

E cottage

a

b

c

d

e

 Draw a plan of your home. Try to imagine what it looks like from above.

How do I draw a route map of my journey to school?

 Investigate and colour Sapna's mind pictures of her route to school.

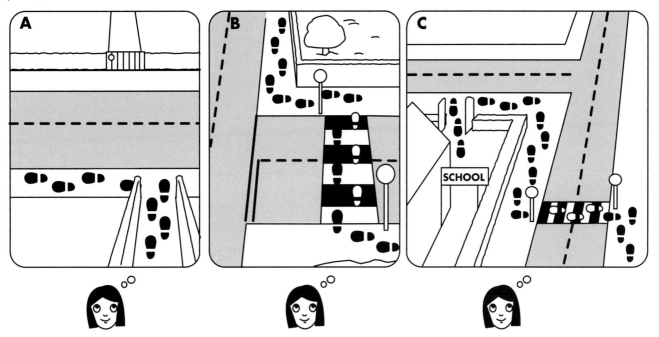

Now complete the route map. Mark Sapna's route with arrows.

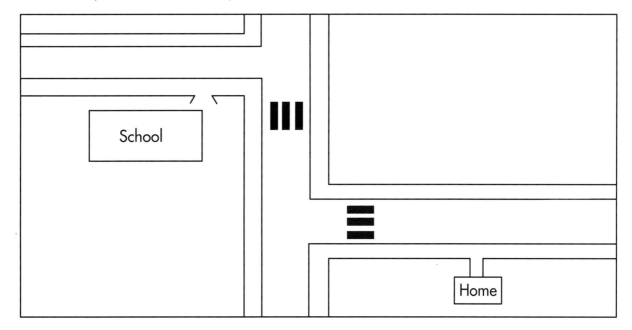

Which way does Sapna turn outside her home to go to school?

. . . . (left, right)

 Draw a mind picture of your own journey to school.
Now draw a route map of your journey.

name

How do I draw a plan of the playground?

 Colour the picture of the playground.

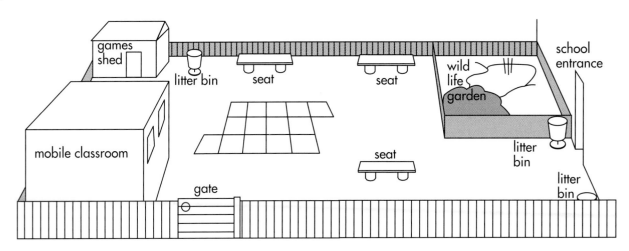

 Investigate the plan of the playground. It has been drawn to scale on centimetre squared paper. **1 square is really 1 pace on the ground.**

Count the squares to find how many paces long the playground is . . . . . paces

Count the squares to find how many paces wide the playground is . . . . . paces

Two things are missing. Can you draw them in the correct position?
Remember! A plan is a bird's eye view.

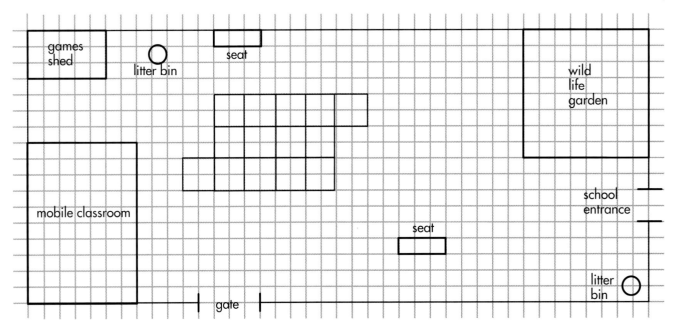

 Now measure your playground by counting how many paces along each side. Make a rough sketch of the position of everything. Draw a plan of your playground to scale using squared paper.

What is a magnetic compass used for?

For hundreds of years travellers have used magnetic compasses to find their way. The magnetic needle in a compass always points close to the north pole. This is called magnetic north.

 Look at this four-point compass face.

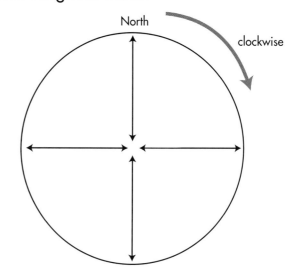

When you are facing north:

north is *up*
east is *right*
south is *down*
west is *left*

North is marked on the compass.
Mark east, south and west.

An easy way to remember the clockwise order of compass directions is to say

Never Ever Sunny Weather
This is called a mnemonic.

This arrow shows north.

Mark the direction shown by these arrows. Use the letters N, E, S and W.

a ⟵ . . . .   b ⟶ . . . .

c ↓ . . . .   d ↑ . . . .

 Make up your own mnemonic to help you remember the clockwise order of compass directions.

N. . . . . E . . . . S . . . . W . . . .

What is an eight-point compass?

 Investigate old maps to find beautifully designed compass roses like this one. Colour the compass rose.

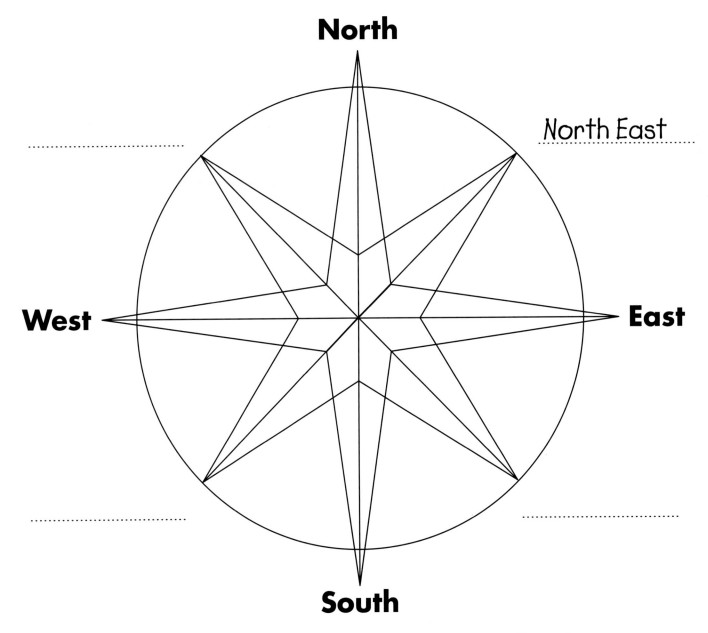

North

North East

West

East

South

1 The direction half way between north and east is   north-east . . . .

2 The direction half way between south and east is   . . . .

3 The direction half way between south and west is   . . . .

4 The direction half way between north and west is   . . . .

 In which direction are you looking through your classroom window? Practise using a real magnetic compass.

What is a grid?

Colour these scattered
shapes.

Sun

star

Moon

Earth

Jupiter

Rocket

satellite

The shapes are in the same
positions but now they are
covered by a *grid*.

Each square on the grid can
now be given a name.

The name of each square is
a letter at the bottom of each
column and a number at the
end of each row.

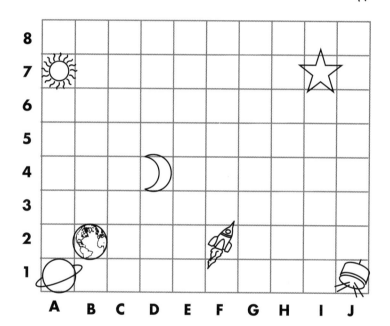

The positions of all the objects can now be given names.

 Investigate this grid . . .

The position of Jupiter is square **A1**. The letter comes before the number.
Can you name the positions of the other objects?

1 Sun   . . . .

2 star   . . . .

3 Moon . . . .

4 satellite . . . .

5 rocket . . . .

6 Earth   . . . .

 Find out about maps called Ordnance Survey maps.
An Ordnance Survey map is divided into grid squares.

What is a symbol?

There is not much room on a plan or a map to write lots of words. Instead pictures or *symbols* can be used.

This symbol means sunny weather on a weather map.

sunny weather

What might these symbols mean on a weather map?

A . . . .

B . . . .

C . . . .

Investigate weather maps on television and in newspapers. Are the same symbols used on all of them?
Draw your own symbols to show:

snowy weather	strong winds
rain showers	hailstones

 Observe the weather daily and use symbols to keep a weather chart.

 Talk about the weather with a friend. What kind of weather do you like? What do you do when it snows?

Can I use symbols on a plan?

Read the story of
Goldilocks and the Three Bears.
Colour the picture of the
three bears' cottage.

What does Goldilocks find
inside the cottage?

Find out by investigating
the *symbols* on the plan.
Look at the *key* to find
what the symbols mean.

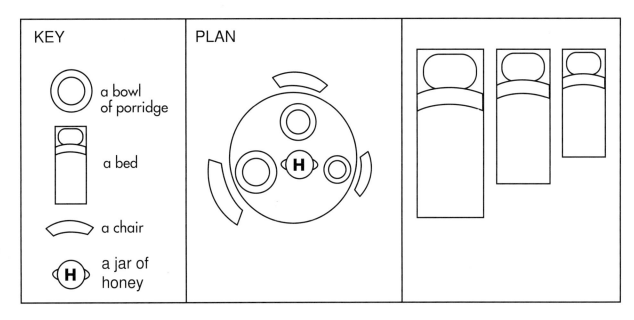

Colour the symbols on the plan:

1   Colour the symbol for Baby Bear's chair yellow.
2   Colour the symbol for Mother Bear's chair red.
3   Colour the symbol for Father Bear's chair green.
4   Colour the symbol for the biggest bed green.
5   Colour the symbol for the smallest bed yellow.
6   Colour the symbol for the middle-sized bed red.
7   Colour the symbol for the smallest bowl of porridge yellow.
8   Colour the symbol for the biggest bowl of porridge green.
9   Colour the symbol for Mother Bear's bowl of porridge red.

10   What is in the jar in the middle of the table?. . . . .

Symbols are used on Ordnance Survey street plans. Investigate the symbols used.

Does colour make symbols easier to understand?

On a plan or a map symbols are used instead of words. The meaning of the symbols is explained in a special box next to the map called a *key*.

A key is also called a *legend*.

We recognise symbols from their shape and colour.

1 Colour the symbol for a pond blue.
2 Colour the symbol for a river blue.
3 Colour the symbol for hills brown.
4 Colour the symbol for a road red.
5 Colour the symbol for a wood green.

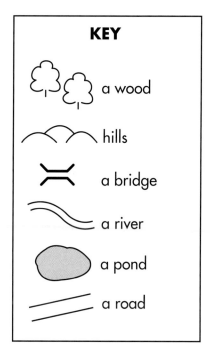

Now find the same symbols on the map below.

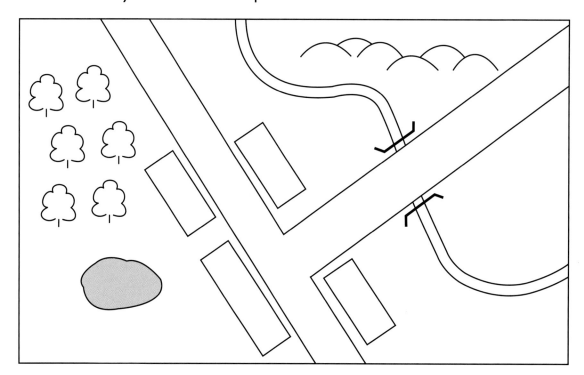

Colour the symbols on the map in the same colours as the symbols in the key.

 On Ordnance Survey maps, lines in different colours mean different things. Find out what brown lines mean.

What kind of information is shown on a street plan or map?

Investigate symbols used on Ordnance Survey plans and maps.

A symbol is an easy way to show information on a plan or map. In towns and cities we may want to show where telephone boxes and bus stops are. We may want to show what buildings are used for.

This could be the symbol for a telephone box.

This could be the symbol for a hospital.

Design symbols for:

a litter bin	a bus stop
a church	a school

 Find out what the symbol for a church is on an Ordnance Survey map. What do you notice?

Can a map help tell a story?

A map can help tell a story. This map tells part of the Red Riding Hood story. Can you see what is happening to Red Riding Hood from this map?

 Look at the map. Colour the map.

 Investigate the key to find what the symbols mean.
Look at the compass rose to find in which direction Red Riding Hood is walking.

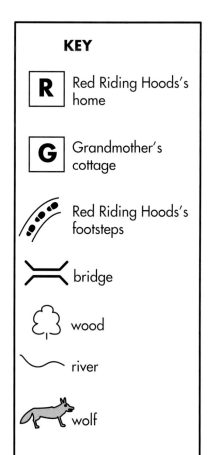

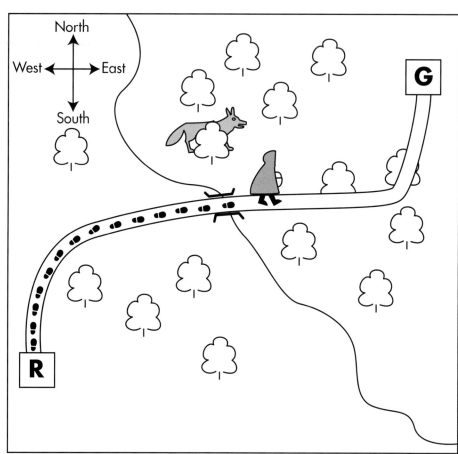

1 In which direction is Red Riding Hood walking? . . . .

(north, east, south, west)

2 Who is hiding behind the tree? . . . .

3 How does Red Riding Hood cross the river? . . . .

Draw a picture to show what happens next in the story of Red Riding Hood.

 Choose your favourite story and draw a map to show what happens in one part of the story.

name

 ## Where do you live?

A map shows a larger area than a plan. A map can show where people live.

 Look at the photographs below.

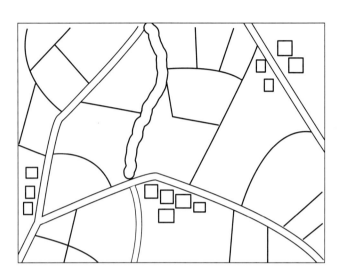

Colour the houses on the plan.
In the countryside there are *few* houses.
Some people live in villages. Some people live in hamlets.
A hamlet is a very small village.

Colour the houses on the plan.
In towns and cities there are *many* houses.
Cities are much bigger than towns. Cities have lots of roads and streets full of buildings of all kinds.

Some people live in the country. Some people live in towns and cities.
Where do you live?

I live in a . . . .(hamlet, village, town, city)

How do I give directions?

 Look at the street plan of Bigglesworth town.

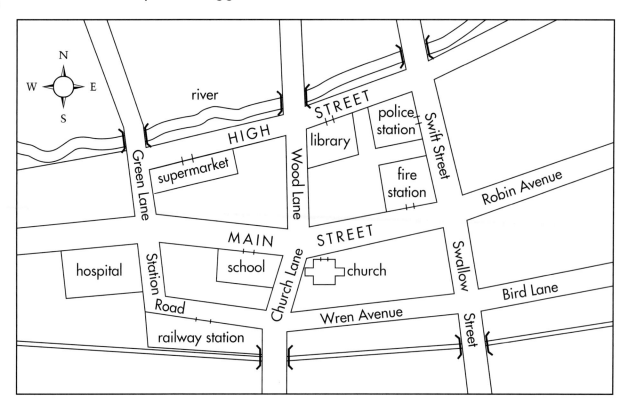

Now follow the instructions on the route card to discover your mystery destination.

Draw your route on the map using arrows.

Start at the library.

 Give directions for a shorter route from the library to school.

 Ask your friend to follow your directions from the school to another mystery destination.

ROUTE CARD

END

8 Turn right into Main Street, walk east to SCHOOL.

7 Walk north to the hospital.

6 Turn right into Station Road, walk west to the railway station.

5

4 Turn left into Church Lane, walk south to Station Road.

3 Turn right into Main Street, walk west to the Church.

2 Turn right into Swift Street, walk south to the Fire Station.

1 Turn right, walk along the High Street to the Police Station.

* **START HERE** at the Library

What is scale?

Remember: 10 millimetres = 1 centimetre

10 millimetres   1 centimetre

These are *real* measurements.

Millimetres and **centimetres** are used to measure *small* things.

But we cannot draw very long lines to their *real* size on a small piece of paper like this.

Instead we draw very long lines to *scale*.

This is a scale: 1 centimetre = 10 centimetres

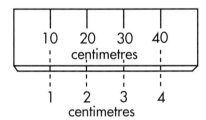

On this scale, 1 centimetre on the paper is *really* 10 centimetres.

These straight lines have been drawn to the scale
1 centimetre = 10 centimetres. How long are they really?

1 ——————————————————

This line *measures* . . . . centimetres.   It is *really* . . . . centimetres long.

2 —————————————————————

This line *measures* . . . . centimetres.   It is *really* . . . . centimetres long.

 How long and how wide is your desk (table)?
Draw a scale plan of your desk. Use the scale 1 centimetre stands for
10 centimetres.

Why are maps drawn to scale?

To measure *big* things we use units called **metres**.
To measure *long* distances we use units called **kilometres**.

100 centimetres = 1 metre
1000 metres = 1 kilometre

On a small piece of paper like this we cannot draw the *real* size of a metre or a kilometre. Instead we use a **scale**.

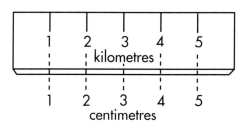

The scale is **1 centimetre = 1 kilometre.**

How far apart are these buildings really?

1

The line measures . . . . centimetres.

The distance between the buildings is really . . . . kilometres.

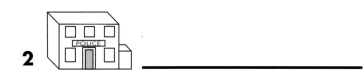

2

The line measures . . . . centimetres.

The distance between the two buildings is really . . . . kilometres.

3

The line measures . . . . centimetres.

The distance between the two buildings is really . . . . kilometres.

 Look at a street plan of your locality. What is the scale?
Measure the distance on the plan between your home and your school.
You may need to use string. How far is it really?

Does a flat map show the world as it really is?

a globe

Investigate a globe. Move it around.
Can you see the whole world at once?
This is what astronauts in space
see when they look down at Earth.

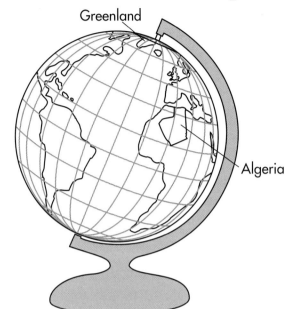

Greenland

Algeria

A globe is a 3D map of the world
because it is round like the real Earth.

1 Colour Algeria and Greenland red.
2 Colour the oceans blue.
3 Colour the rest of the land green.

a map

A flat map does not show the world as it really is.

Imagine the world as a round orange.

Take the peel off an orange in one piece and try to lay it down flat.
You can only lay it flat by breaking the peel.
The same thing happens when the round world is drawn on a flat map.

making maps

The size of countries drawn to scale on a flat map does not always look correct.
Look again at the globe at the top of the page. You can see that Algeria, in
Africa, and Greenland are both about the same size in real life.

Now look at the flat map of the
world.
Colour Algeria and
Greenland red.
Colour the oceans blue.
Colour the rest of the
land green.

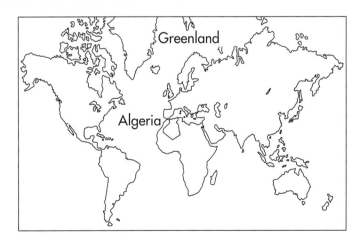

Greenland

Algeria

Do Algeria and Greenland look the same size now? . . . .

Are Algeria and Greenland the same size in real life? . . . .

How do I use an atlas index?

You will need an atlas for this activity.

 Investigate your atlas index. What do you notice?
An atlas is a book of maps. We look in the index at the back of an atlas to find where places are. The names of all the places are arranged in alphabetical order like a dictionary.

a b c d e f g h i j k l m n o p q r s t u v w x y z

1 Put the names of these British cities in alphabetical order. Then find where they are by looking in the atlas index for the page number. Then turn to the correct page. See if you can find the cities.

London . . . .

Aberdeen . . . .

Birmingham . . . .

Dublin . . . .

2 The names of these places all begin with the same first letter. To put them in alphabetical order you must look at the *second* letter of each name.
Then find where they are by looking in the atlas index for the page number. Then turn to the correct page.

Bristol . . . .

Bath . . . .

Belfast . . . .

Birmingham . . . .

3 The names of these places all begin with the same first and second letters. To put them in alphabetical order you must look at the *third* letter.

Tenby . . . .

Tewkesbury . . . .

Tebworth . . . .

Teddington . . . .

31 The United Kingdom

What is the United Kingdom?

The **United Kingdom** is the countries of England, Scotland, Wales and Northern Ireland. The Republic of Ireland is not part of the United Kingdom. The British Isles means both the United Kingdom and the Republic of Ireland or Eire.

Investigate an atlas to find where you live in the British Isles. If you live in a big city or town you will find it in the atlas. *Remember to look in the index first.* If you live in a small village or hamlet, look for the nearest big city or town to your home. *Put a red cross in the right place on your outline map.*

On the outline map of the British Isles:

1 Colour the seas and rivers blue.

2 Colour the Republic of Ireland green.

3 Colour England, Scotland, Wales and Northern Ireland yellow.

Look at the scale bar. On this map 1 centimetre is really 50 kilometres.

The line joining London and Cardiff measures . . . . cm.

What is the real distance between London and Cardiff? . . . . km.

How far is it from London to Edinburgh? . . . . km.

Can you find out which plant symbol belongs with which country of the United Kingdom?

1 . . . .

2 . . . .

3 . . . .

4 . . . .

Write your answers and colour the plant symbols.

Continued on next page

N

SCOTLAND

Edinburgh

NORTH SEA

NORTHERN
IRELAND

Belfast

IRISH SEA

REPUBLIC OF
IRELAND

R. Trent

ENGLAND

WALES

R. Severn

Cardiff

London

R. Thames

ENGLISH CHANNEL

Scale bar

0   50   100 km

What is the Union flag?

 The Union flag is the flag of the United Kingdom.

Look at the colour key.
Colour the flags of each country.

The flags of England, Scotland and Northern Ireland have been put together to make the Union flag.

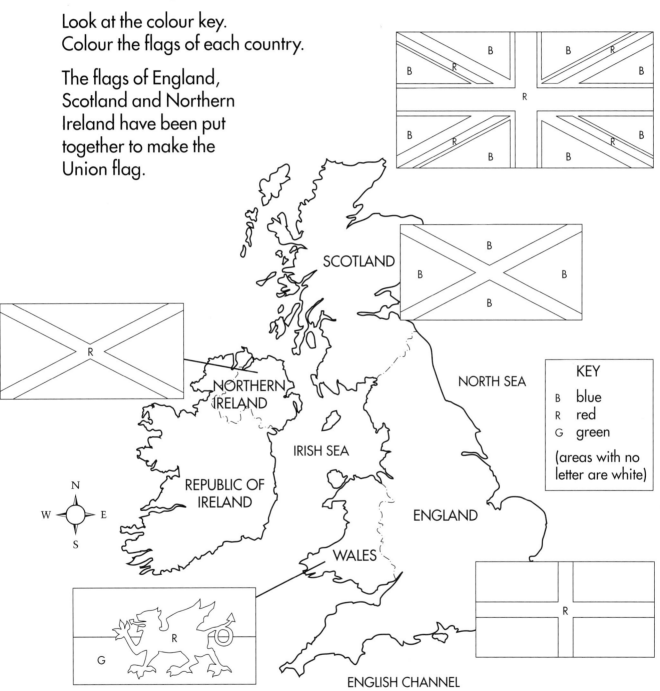

KEY

B blue
R red
G green

(areas with no letter are white)

I live in . . . . (England, Scotland, Northern Ireland, Wales)

 Look at photographs of people and places in each of the countries of the United Kingdom. What can you learn from them?

33 Continents

name

What is a continent?

Look at the jigsaw pieces below. Each piece is the shape of a continent.
A continent is a mass of land. Colour each shape a different colour. Cut out the
shapes and fit them together like a jigsaw by glueing them on to an outline map
of the world.

There are seven main continents:

Europe, Asia, Africa, Oceania, Antarctica, South America, North America

Can you label your map? Use an atlas to help you.

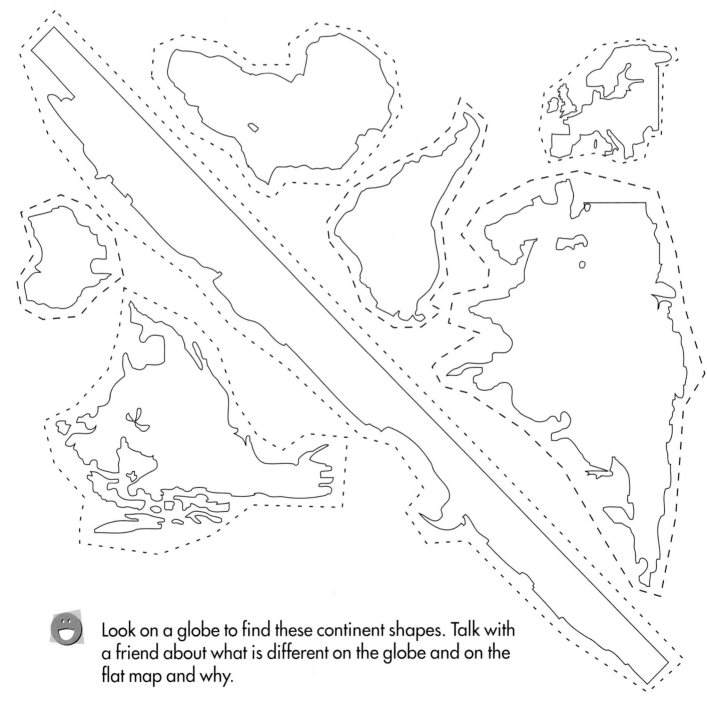

Look on a globe to find these continent shapes. Talk with
a friend about what is different on the globe and on the
flat map and why.

Continued on next page

name

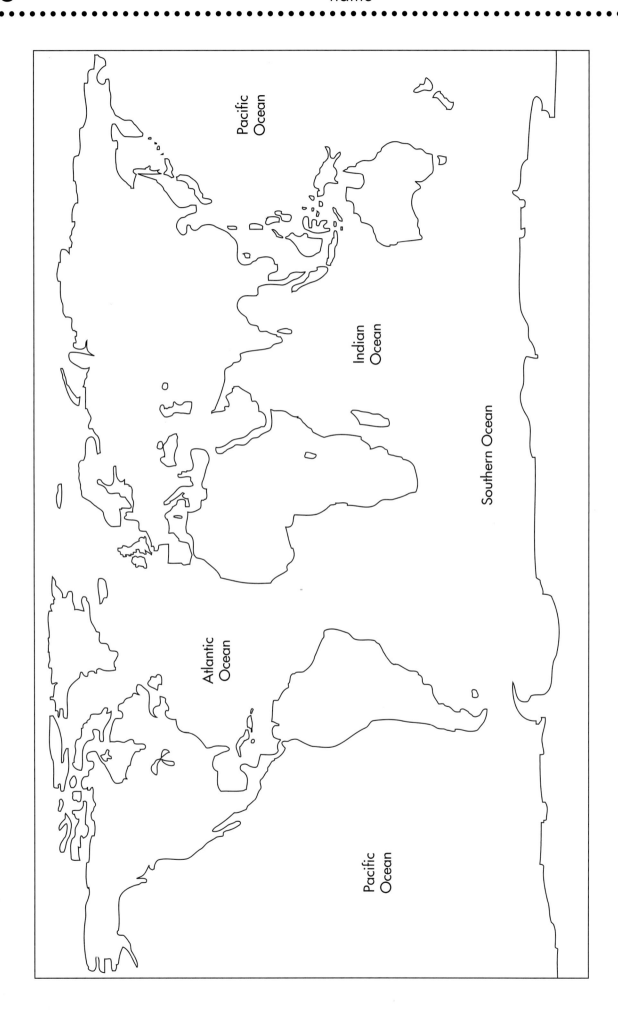

What is the difference between a continent and a country?

 Investigate a map of the **continent** of Europe in an atlas. Now look at these shapes. Each shape is a **continent**. A continent is a large land mass. Colour **green** the **continent** which is **Europe**.
What are the others called?

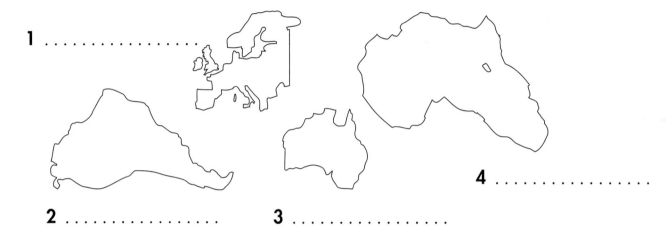

1 . . . .

2 . . . .   3 . . . .   4 . . . .

Continents are divided into countries. The shapes below are some of the **countries** of Europe.

1 Colour **red** the shape that matches the real shape of the **British Isles**.

2 Now find a shape that looks like a boot. This is the real shape of **Italy**. Colour the shape of Italy **yellow**.

3 The two countries of **Spain** and **Portugal** together make a rough square shape. Colour them both **blue**.

Now find these countries in the atlas.

 Look again at the map of Europe in your atlas. Can you find out which 15 countries belong to the European Union? Find out more about the EU.

35 Europe

name

What is a capital city?

Look at the outline map of Europe and the key.

Large circles have been used to show the positions of big **cities**.
Colour all the circles **red**.
These red circles are **symbols**.
The most important city in a country is called a **capital city**.
The capital city of England is London.
The capital city of France is Paris.
The capital city of Spain is Madrid.
The capital city of Italy is Rome.
Write the name of each capital city on the map next to the red circle.

Use an atlas to find these answers:
1 What is the capital city of Portugal? . . . .
2 What is the capital city of Greece? . . . .
3 What is the capital city of Germany? . . . .
4 What is the capital city of the Netherlands? . . . .

Find these capital cities on a map of Europe in an atlas. Which of these cities
have been built close to a large river? London stands on the River Thames.
Why are cities built close to rivers?

Find colour pictures of these flags in an atlas or an information book. Colour the
flags to match.

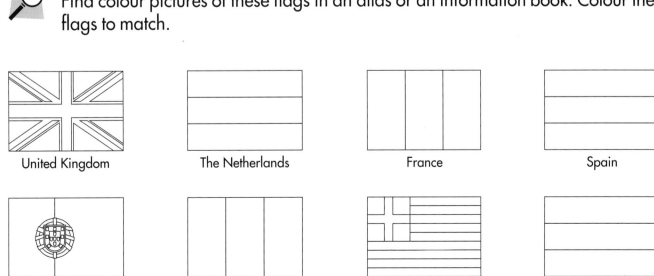

United Kingdom   The Netherlands   France   Spain

Portugal   Italy   Greece   Germany

Continued on next page

35 Europe

name

KEY

○ city

– · – · – borders
between countries

UK

THE
NETHERLANDS

L

A

B

GERMANY

P

PORTUGAL

FRANCE

ITALY

M

R

L

SPAIN

GREECE

A

36 Animals of the world in danger   name

 ## Which wild animals are endangered?

 Investigate the pictures and chart. These animals are endangered. Colour the pictures of the animals. Cut out the pictures. Glue them on to the map of the world in the right places.

endangered animal	continent where found
otter	Europe
puma	North America
jaguar	South America
giant tortoise	Oceania
tiger	Asia
blue whale	Antarctica
gorilla	Africa

jaguar

puma

gorilla

otter

blue whale

giant tortoise

tiger

 Investigate wildlife in the British Isles.

Use information books or a CD Rom encyclopedia to find out which animals are endangered in Britain. Choose one to write about here. Draw a picture too.

. . . .

. . . .

. . . .

. . . .

. . . .

. . . .

 Talk about wildlife in your locality. What could you do to protect the wildlife in your garden or school grounds?

Continued on next page

36 Animals of the world in danger   name

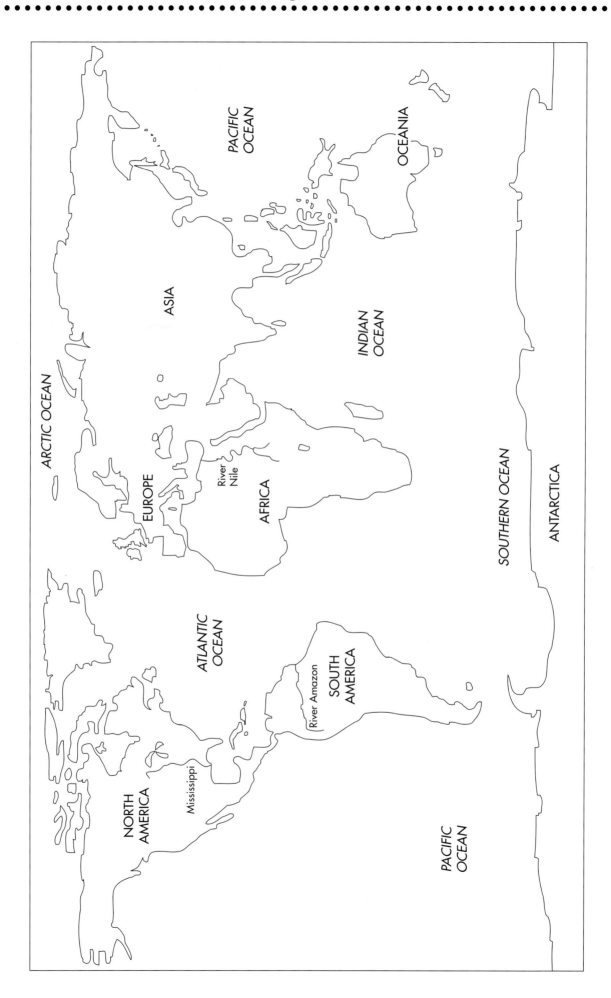

What is a grid reference?

Investigate and colour the treasure island map.

A grid of *lines* has been placed over the map. Each *line* on the grid has been given a number. We can name the position of everything on the island by using these numbers. Every position is given two numbers. The first number is from the bottom of the map and the second number from the side of the map. The place where the *lines* meet is called the **grid reference**.
The hut is at grid reference 2, 1.

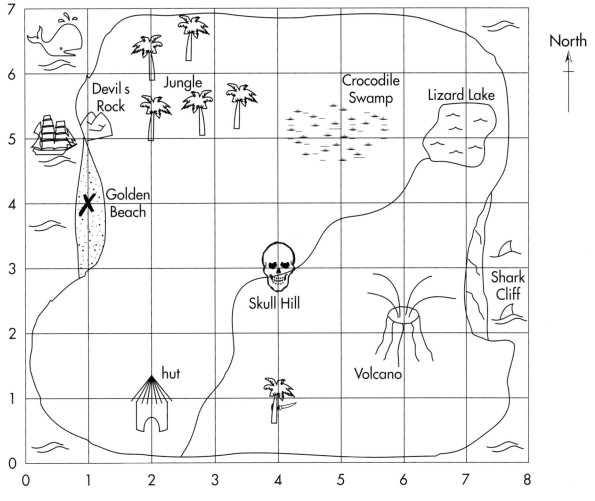

1 What can you see at grid reference 6, 2? . . . .

2 What can you see at grid reference 7, 5? . . . .

3 What can you see at grid reference 4, 3? . . . .

The pirate is behind the tree at grid reference 4, 1. To reach the treasure he must go north to Skull Hill at 4, 3. Then east to 5, 3. Then he must go north to the crocodile swamp at 5,5 and west to the rock at 1, 5 and finally south to the treasure on the beach at 1, 4.

Draw arrows to mark the pirate's route.

Where do bananas grow?

Look on the map. Find the equator. Now find the islands of the West Indies. Look at photographs of the West Indies. Bananas grow there because it is hot and wet. The West Indies are *far* from the U.K. Bananas from the West Indies are sent by ship to the British Isles.

Which way?

The ship travels in a direction half way between north and east.

This direction is called . . . .

Bananas are also grown in Africa, South America and South East Asia. Draw a banana on your map in these places.

Collect sticky labels from the bananas that you buy from the supermarket. The names of the countries they come from are printed on the labels.

The journey of a yellow banana

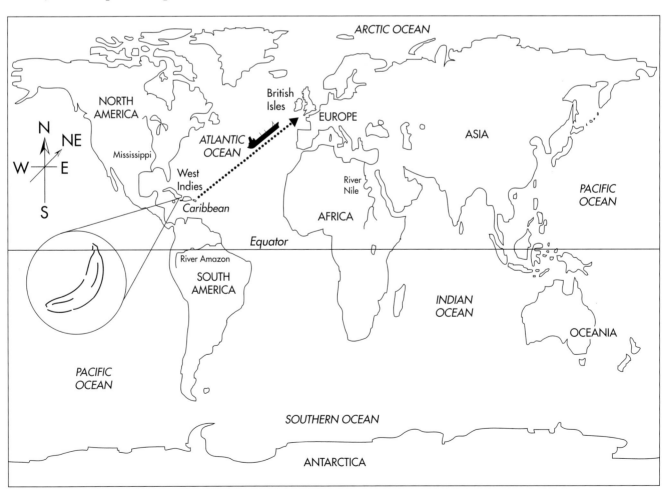

Answers

. . . .

1 1 The car is *near* the toy box.
2 The car is *in* the toy box.
3 The car is *far from* the toy box.
4 The car is *under* the toy box.
5 The car is *on* the toy box.
6 The car is *behind* the toy box.
7 The car is *in front of* the toy box.

3 B right
C left
D right

Maze Start: up, left, second left, right, right, right, right, left, left, left, left, right, right, right.

5 spoon and butter are both missing from the plan.

6 1 5 tables **2** 3 cupboards **3** green **4** red **5** orange
6 Swarupa **7** Stephen **8** Frances
9 cupboard **10** Sapna.

7 1 Tree A is bigger than tree B.
2 Tree B is smaller than tree A.

1 Tree C is the biggest.
2 Tree H is the smallest.
3 F, G and H are coloured green
4 C, D and E are coloured orange.

1 c is yellow **2** a is red **3** b is blue.

8 the book is 5 toy bricks long

10 a 4cm **b** 3cm **c** 2cm
A 5cm **B** 7cm **C** 3cm **D** 10cm
D is the longest line. C is the shortest line.

12 A 5cm **B** 3cm **C** 1cm

13 a supermarket – go shopping; **b** church – say a prayer
c cinema – watch a film **d** garage – buy petrol

14 2 cars, 3 petrol pumps
Plans and buildings: Ac Be Ca Db Ed

15 Sapna turns left.

16 40 paces long / 17 paces wide
1 seat and 1 litter bin are missing from the plan.

17

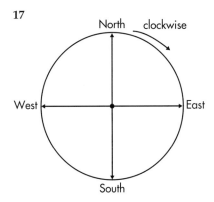

a west **b** east **c** south **d** north

18

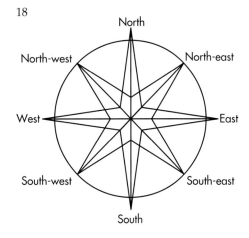

1 north-east **2** south-east **3** south-west
4 north-west

19 1 Sun A7 **2** Star I7 **3** Moon D4 **4** Satellite Jl
5 Rocket F2 **6** Earth B2

20 A cloud **B** thunder and lightning **C** rain

21 10 Honey

24 1 East, then north **2** Wolf **3** Over the bridge

26

Route Card
END
↓ Cross over Main Street, to reach <u>SCHOOL</u>
└→ Turn left and walk down Wood Lane.
← Turn left and walk to the corner. Cross over Wood Lane.
* Start Here at the <u>LIBRARY</u>

27 1 7cm 70cm **2** 10cm 100cm (1 m)

28 1 8cm 8km **2** 6cm 6km **3** 4cm 4km

29 No. Yes.

30 1 Aberdeen, Birmingham, Dublin, London
2 Bath, Belfast, Birmingham, Bristol
3 Tebworth, Teddington, Tenby, Tewkesbury

31 London to Cardiff 4cm / 200km.
London to Edinburgh 525 km.
1 Wales
2 Northern Ireland [and Eire]
3 England
4 Scotland

34 1 Europe
   2 South America
   3 Australia
   4 Africa

   EU countries: UK, Ireland, France, Belgium, Netherlands, Luxembourg, Germany, Denmark, Sweden, Finland, Spain, Portugal, Greece, Italy, Austria

35 1 Lisbon **2** Athens **3** Berlin **4** Amsterdam (The Hague is the centre of Government)

37 6,2 Volcano
   7,5 Lizard Lake
   4,3 Skull Hill

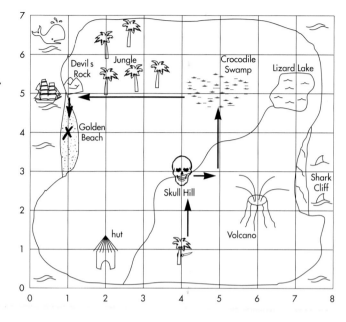